One-minute timer

**Work with a friend.
Use a one-minute timer.**

1 In one minute,
how many crosses
can you make?

_____ crosses

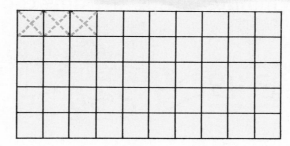

2 In one minute,
how many numbers
can you write?

What is your last
number? _____

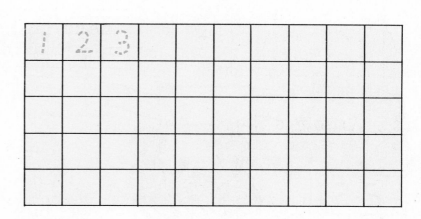

3 In one minute, how many times can you

 hop _____

 bounce a ball _____

 skip _____

 step on and off a bench? _____

4 Start the one-minute timer and close your eyes.
Put up your hand when you think one minute has passed.
Check the timer.

Do the same for two minutes.

Going to the station

two o'clock — **2:00**

two 'o' three — **2:03**

two twenty fi[ve] — **2:25**

↑ This number shows the **hour.**

These numbers show the **minutes past the hour.**

1 As each minute passes, the time changes. Write the times.

2:49 **2:50** **2:** **:**

: **:** **:** **2:53**

2:57 **:** **:** **3:00** **3:01**

There are 60 minutes in 1 hour.

1 minute after **2:59** is **3:00**

2 Write these times.

One minute **before**   One minute **after**

: ← **3:59** → **:**

: ← **5:00** → **:**

HEINEMANN MATHEMATICS 3

Name

MEASURE, SHAPE and HANDLING DATA WORKBOOK

Revised

What time is it?

1   Match the times.

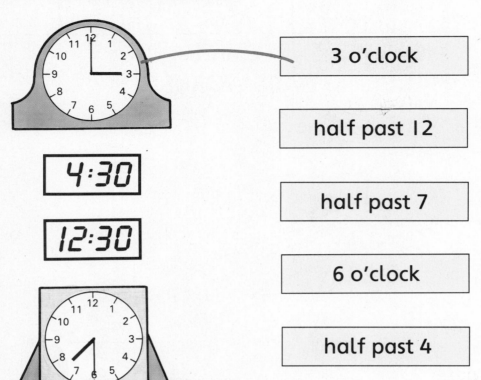

3 o'clock

half past 12

half past 7

6 o'clock

half past 4

2   Write the times.

2 o'clock

:

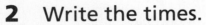

:

:

:

:

On the train

three ten

The train left at 10 minutes after 3 o'clock.

The train left at | 10 minutes past 3 | .

1 Write these times.

minutes past

minutes past

minutes past

minutes past

minutes past

minutes past

2 Where was the train at half past four? _____

Problem solving

3 At 10 minutes past 4, what had the train just passed? _____

H48

Sponsored silence

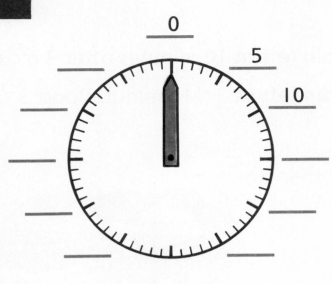

0
5
10

I The hour timer is marked in minutes. Complete by counting in fives.

2 Write the number of minutes each child was silent.

Tim

_____ minutes

Ann

_____ minutes

Joe

_____ minutes

Salma

_____ minutes

Mira

_____ minutes

Jan

_____ minutes

Extension

3 Who was silent for 30 minutes longer than Tim? _____

The sponsored silence started at 9 o'clock.

Rajan talked

after __10__ minutes.

The time was __10__ minutes past __9__ .

1 The clocks show when some other children talked.
Write their times.

Gail talked

after __13__ minutes.

Time: ___ minutes past __9__ .

Ken talked

after ___ minutes.

Time: ___ minutes past __9__ .

Lena talked

after ___ minutes.

Time: ___ minutes past ___ .

Pam talked

after ___ minutes.

Time: ___ minutes past ___ .

Lenny talked

after ___ minutes.

Time: _____ .

Jack talked

after ___ minutes.

Time: _____ .

Problem solving

2 Which children were still silent at half past nine?

_____

At the Sports Centre

Mark arrived 40 minutes after 2 o'clock.

He arrived at __40__ minutes past __2__.

I Complete these times.

____ minutes past ____

____ minutes past ____

____ minutes past ____

____ minutes past ____

____ minutes past ____

____ minutes past ____

Problem solving

2 Where was Mark at half past three? _____

Where was Mark at half past four? _____

Go to Textbook page 27

Metres

Work with a partner.   Use a metre stick.

1   Are you taller or shorter than 1 metre? _____

2   Is your stretch
longer than 1 metre? _____

Is your shoulder height
shorter than 1 metre? _____

Work in the classroom or hall.

3   Find two objects which are about 1 metre long.

Name them. _____   _____

4

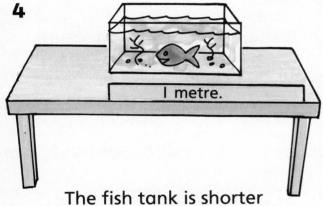

The fish tank is shorter
than 1 metre.

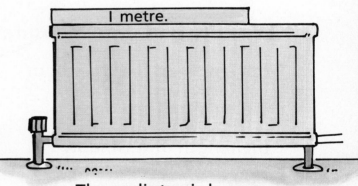

The radiator is longer
than 1 metre.

Name two objects which you think are
shorter than 1 metre.   longer than 1 metre.

_____   _____

_____   _____

Check using your metre stick.

Investigation

5   Find out if you can jump
further than 1 metre.

Measuring

I metre can be written as 1m

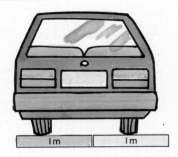

The car is **about** 4 m long.

It is **about** 2 m wide.

Work with a partner.

Use a metre stick.

I Estimate and then measure

	Estimate	Measure
the length of the classroom	about m	about m
the height of the door	about m	about m
the length of a window	about m	about m
	about m	about m

Which one is longest? _____ shortest? _____

Work in the hall or corridor.

2 Go forward.
Stop when you
think you have
walked 4 m.

Make a
mark (X).

Measure how
far you walked.

About_____ m.

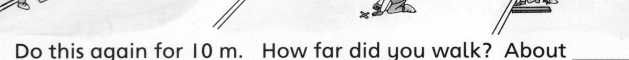

Do this again for 10 m. How far did you walk? About _____ m.

Half metres

1   Ask your teacher for a 1 metre strip.   Fold it in half and cut.   Label your half metre strips like this.

half metre   half metre

Use a half metre strip.

2   Find two objects which are about one half metre long. Name them.

_____   _____

one half metre can be written as $\frac{1}{2}$ m

3

The lamp is shorter than $\frac{1}{2}$ m

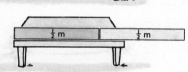

The table is longer than $\frac{1}{2}$ m but shorter than 1 m.

Name two objects which you think are
    shorter than $\frac{1}{2}$ m

longer than $\frac{1}{2}$ m but shorter than 1 m.

_____   _____

_____   _____

Check using your half metre strips.

4

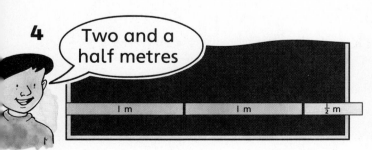

Two and a half metres

1 m   1 m $\frac{1}{2}$ m

The width of the board is about $2\frac{1}{2}$ m.
Use metre sticks and a half metre strip to measure some objects in the classroom.

width of board	about $2\frac{1}{2}$ m		

Centimetres

Use centimetre sticks like this one.

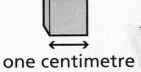

one centimetre

1 Measure these lengths.

length of my pencil	about	centimetres
width of this page	about	centimetres
width of my thumb	about	centimetres

2 Choose an object and measure its length.

_____ about _____ centimetres

I centimetre can be written as I cm

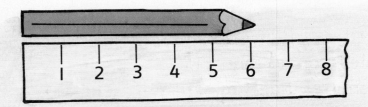

The length of this pencil is about 6 cm.

3 Use a centimetre ruler.

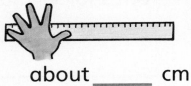
length of my span

about _____ cm

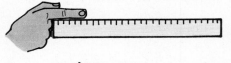
length of my first finger

about _____ cm

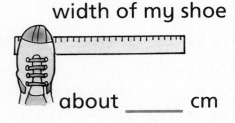
width of my shoe

about _____ cm

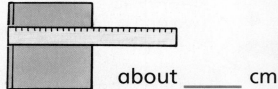
width of my book

about _____ cm

Investigation

4 In your group, what is the difference in length

between the **longest** and **shortest** spans? _____

Fish tank

1 Estimate and then measure in centimetres the length of each fish.

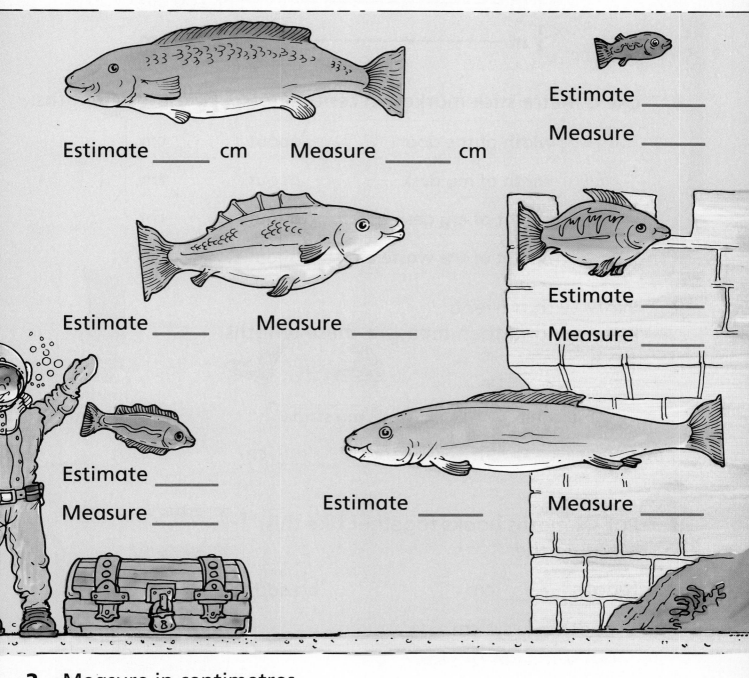

Estimate _____ cm   Measure _____ cm

Estimate _____

Measure _____

Estimate _____

Measure _____

Estimate _____

Measure _____

Estimate _____

Measure _____

Estimate _____   Measure _____

2 Measure in centimetres.

height of the castle _____   height of the diver _____

depth of the water _____   length of the chest _____

3 Draw and colour a fish 6 cm long.

Cut it out and stick it in the tank.

Centimetres and metres

is the same length as		
1 m ⟶	100 cm	
½ m ⟶	50 cm	

1 Use a metre stick marked in centimetres. Find these lengths.

width of the door	about	cm
width of my desk	about	cm
height of my desk	about	cm
height of the waste bin	about	cm

2 Work with a friend.
Estimate and then measure these lengths.

my cubit

my stride

height to
my knee

about _____ cm   about _____ cm   about _____ cm

3 Put six maths books together like this.
Measure the

length _____ cm

breadth _____ cm

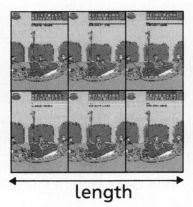

breadth

length

4

Put four maths books side by side in a row.

Measure the length
of the row.   _____ cm

How much longer
than ½ m is this?   _____ cm

My measurements

1 **Use a tape which is marked in centimetres.**

Measure yourself with help from a friend.

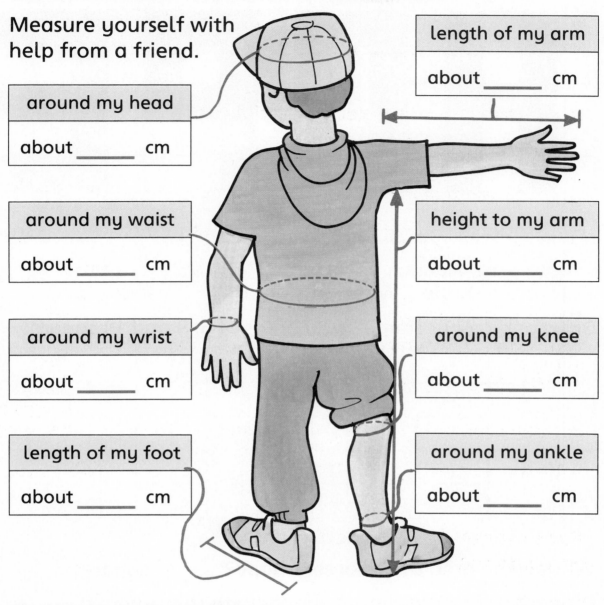

around my head

about _____ cm

length of my arm

about _____ cm

around my waist

about _____ cm

height to my arm

about _____ cm

around my wrist

about _____ cm

around my knee

about _____ cm

length of my foot

about _____ cm

around my ankle

about _____ cm

2 **Find out how far you can**

bunny hop

spread your feet

lift your knee

Me _____ cm

My friend _____ cm

Me _____ cm

My friend _____ cm

Me _____ cm

My friend _____ cm

Go to Textbook page 31

Counting squares

1 Write the area of each letter.

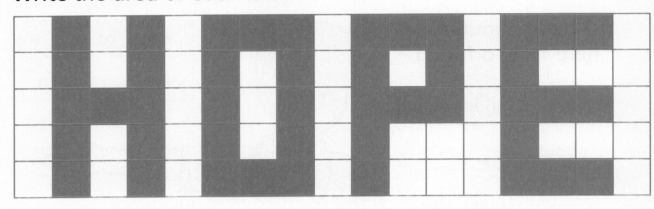

_____ squares   _____ squares   _____ squares   _____ squares

2 Colour the shape.   What is its area? _____ squares.

Draw and colour shapes with areas of 6, 9 and 14 squares.

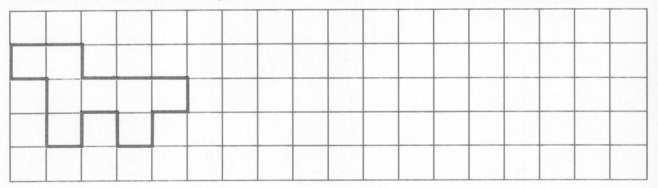

3 What is the area of the green shape? _____ squares.

Draw and colour different shapes with this area.

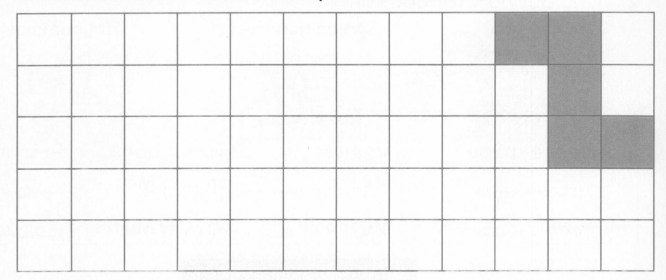

1 Look at the blue shape.

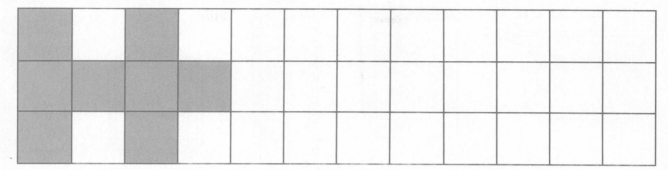

Draw a shape with a **larger** area.   Colour it green.
Draw a shape with a **smaller** area.   Colour it red.

2 Which of the shapes below do you **think** has

the largest area? _____

the smallest area? _____

the same area as the purple shape? _____

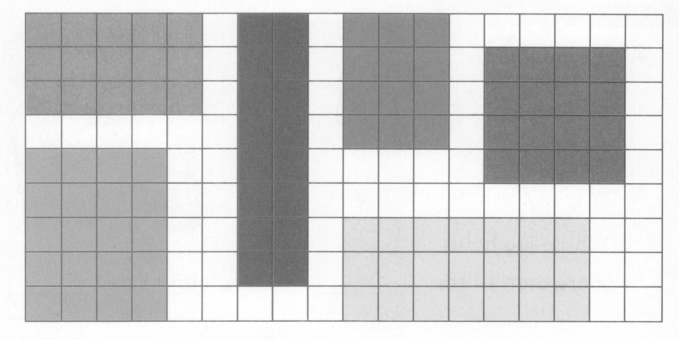

3 Now write the area of each shape.

orange shape _____ squares   brown shape _____ squares

purple shape _____ squares   blue shape _____ squares

green shape _____ squares   yellow shape _____ squares

Go to Textbook page 32

Litres

Each of these containers holds 1 litre.

1 Use a litre measure. Find 2 containers which hold
  more than 1 litre   **less than** 1 litre

_____   _____

_____   _____

Problem solving

2

Joan

Tom

Whose jug holds

more than 1 litre _____   less than 1 litre? _____

3 Supermarkets sell many
  containers which hold 1 litre.

  Make a list of some of these.

  Find out what e means.

Shopping List

1   **You need paper cups, a litre measure
and a kettle.**

How many children can each be given
a paper cupful of lemonade
from 1 litre?   _____

How many paper cupfuls can be
filled from a kettle?   _____

About how many litres do you
think the kettle holds?   _____

2   **You need three large containers and a litre measure.**

I Litre

Estimate and then measure the capacity of each container.

Container	Estimate		Measure	
	about	litres	about	litres
	about	litres	about	litres
	about	litres	about	litres

Ask your teacher what to do next.

Fruit and vegetables

Use a 1 kilogram (1 kg) weight, the bag of shopping and a two-pan balance.

1 Choose an object from the bag. Estimate its weight. Write its name on a shelf.

2 Use the two-pan balance to check your estimate. If it is correct, put a tick. If it is wrong, correct it.

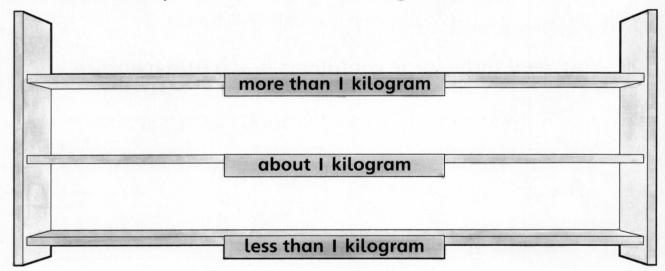

more than 1 kilogram

about 1 kilogram

less than 1 kilogram

3 Do all this again for the other objects in the bag.

4 Fill a plastic bag so that it weighs more than 1 kilogram.

5 Weigh out 1 kilogram of plasticine.

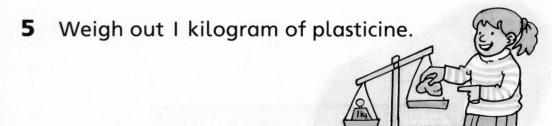

1 Use a two-pan balance.
Make two half kilogram weights
from the 1 kg of plasticine.

2 Put one of your $\frac{1}{2}$ kg weights in one pan
and an object in the other.
Find objects for each part of the table. **Estimate first.**

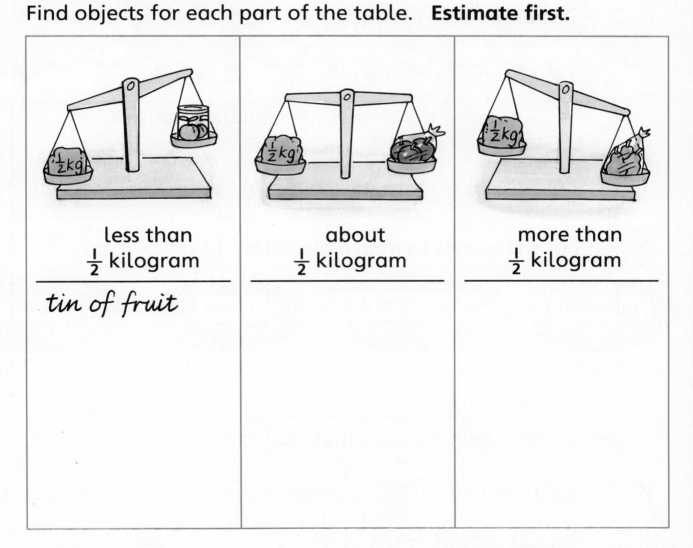

less than $\frac{1}{2}$ kilogram	about $\frac{1}{2}$ kilogram	more than $\frac{1}{2}$ kilogram
tin of fruit		

3 Use the two-pan balance and your $\frac{1}{2}$ kg weight.
Weigh $\frac{1}{2}$ kg of sand into a bag.

Go to Textbook page 33

Cakes and sweets

1 Colour to sort the cakes.

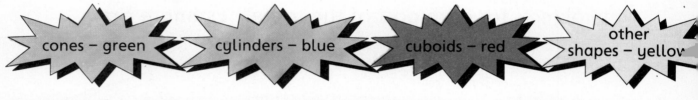

cones – green   cylinders – blue   cuboids – red   other shapes – yellow

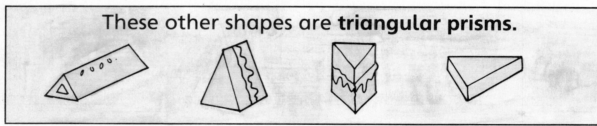

These other shapes are **triangular prisms.**

2 Colour the sweets to match the colour of the plates.

pyramids   triangular prisms   cubes   spheres

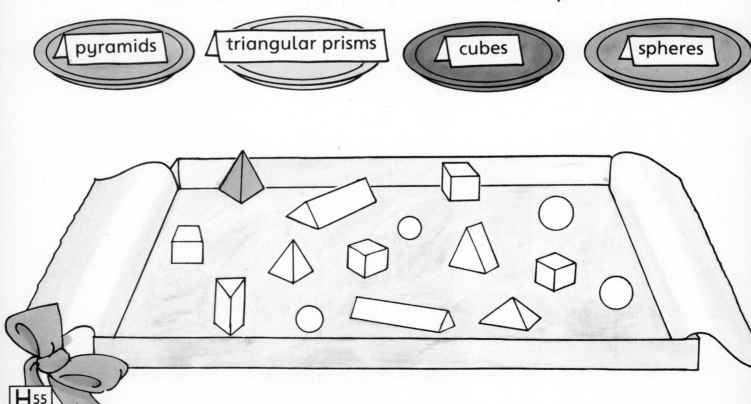

Food and drink

You need shapes like these.
Look at their faces.

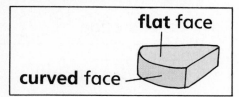

flat face

curved face

1 Match each shape to a label.

all faces are flat

flat faces and
curved faces

all faces are curved

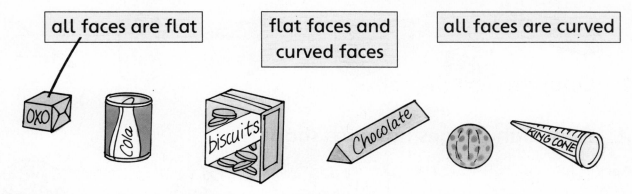

2 Count the faces and complete the table.

shape	OXO	Cola	Chocolate	(ball)	KING CONE	biscuits
flat faces	6					
curved faces	0					
total	6					

3

 4 flat faces
1 curved face

Write about the
faces of these shapes.

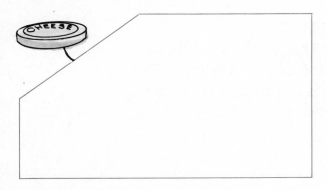

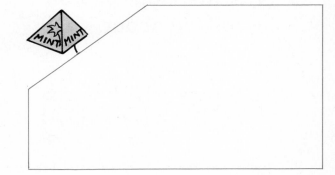

4 Sort out some shapes. Say how you sorted them.

More food and drink

You need your shapes. Look at their **edges**.

straight edge

curved edge

1 Match each shape to a label.

| all edges are straight | straight edges and curved edges | all edges are curved |

2 How many **edges** has each shape?

_____   _____   _____   _____

 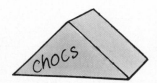  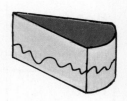

_____   _____   _____   _____

Problem solving

3 Tick the shape Sharon is talking about.

The shape has three faces. Two are flat. One is curved. It has two edges. They are curved.

4 Ask your teacher if you can play the "shape in the bag" game.

You need your shapes.

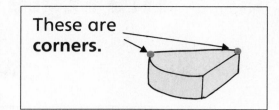
These are **corners.**

1 How many **corners** has each shape?

   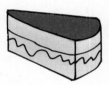

____ ____ ____ ____

____ ____ ____ ____

2    **Each cuboid has**

____ corners

____ faces

____ edges.

   **Each cone has**

____ corners

____ faces

____ edges.

   **Each cylinder has**

____ corners

____ faces

____ edges.

   Each cube has

____ corners

____ faces

____ edges.

Ask your teacher what to do next.

Tile style

1 Complete the brick patterns.

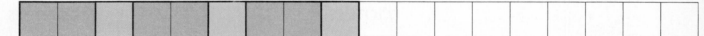

2 Use **squares**. Make the pattern of tiles for the roof. Colour the pattern.

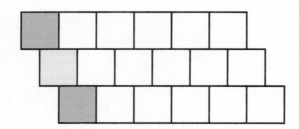

3 Use **rectangles**. Make this pattern of tiles for the kitchen floor. Draw and colour the pattern.

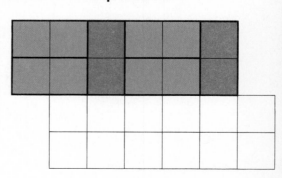

4 Use rectangles. Make some patterns of your own.

All shapes

Some children have said that there are too many  in the All shapes packet. Do you agree?

1 Count the sweets.
Use the tick sheet.

		Total

2 Make a graph of your results.

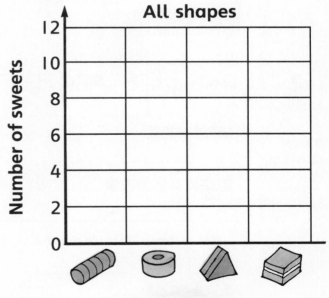

All shapes

Number of sweets

12 10 8 6 4 2 0

Investigation

3 Use a packet of sweets.
Sort them.
What did you find?

Go to Textbook page 41

Measure, Shape and Handling data Workbook: Record of Work

Name _____   Class _____

MSHD Workbook / Textbook / Reinforcement Sheets / Check-ups

Time	W1	W2	W3	W4	W5	W6	W7	R25	T27	R26	T28	R27	T29	Check-up 1

Other activities: T30

Length	W8	W9	W10	W11	W12	W13	W14	T31	Check-up 2

Area	W15	W16	T32	Check-up 3

Volume	W17	W18	Check-up 3

Weight	W19	W20	T33	Check-up 4

Measure: units, investigation	T34	T35	Check-up 4

3D Shape	W21	W22	W23	W24	Check-up 5

Tiling	W25	W26	Check-up 6

Right angles	W27	W28	W29	T36	Check-up 6

Other activities: T37 T38

Symmetry	T39	W30	T40	W31	W32	Check-up 7

Handling data	W33	W34	W35	W36	W37	W38	T41	T42	R28	T43	Check-up 8

Other activities: T44 T45

Published by Heinemann Educational Publishers, Halley Court, Jordan Hill, Oxford OX2 8EJ, a division of Reed Educational and Professional Publishers Ltd.
ISBN 0 435 03781 1 © Scottish Primary Mathematics Group 1992/5.
First published 1992. Revised edition 1995.   98 99   7 6 5 4
Produced by Oxprint Ltd, Oxford. Illustrated by Oxford Illustrators. Printed by Jarrold Printing, Norwich.

ISBN 0-435-03100-7